DAILY BALANCE JOURNAL

3 YEAR DAILY JOURNAL FOR LIFE BALANCE AND SELF-CONNECTION

MIKE ELTGROTH

BeachPath
Press, LLC

ISBN 978-0-9961745-3-4

First Edition, 2016

BeachPath Press, LLC
Visit us online at beachpathpress.com
or email at info@beachpathpress.com

This book is designed to provide accurate and authoritative information with regard to the subject matter covered. It is sold with the understanding that neither the publisher nor author is engaged in rendering legal, accounting, investment or other professional advice. If legal advice or other expert assistance is required, the services of a competent professional should be sought.

This journal belongs to:

_____

If found, please contact at:

_____

Starting year: 20____ and date:_____

Introduction

What would greater balance in your life mean for you? More peace? More time to do the things that you love? More energy? The purpose of this journal is to gently guide you through all aspects of your life in a search for deeper understanding, greater balance, and harmony. A simple daily question format is used with just enough space provided for a thoughtful, yet concise, answer.

The life balance questions are designed to allow you a chance to reflect, dream, seek out what is true for you, realize what makes you happy, and acknowledge what makes you uneasy. Deep down we usually know who we are and what we need, we just have to ask and then listen. Listen very carefully to your inner voice. That voice may be muffled and hard to hear from years of being ignored or drowned out by all of life's commotion but it is still there. Just listen. The first step to gaining more balance is to seek it. And so here you are.

How To Use Your Journal

The framework for your journey is comprised of the seven facets of life. We will rotate through these facets once each week with a new question every day. There is space provided for three years so you can see patterns, trends, and interesting connections that you might otherwise have missed. Most of the questions are thought provoking and not necessarily yes/no answers. Try to write descriptive answers that will engage your thoughts deeper and will therefore have more meaning when you look back at them in the future. There's no need to wait for any particular day to start using your journal such as the first of the year. Simply go to today's date and answer the question.

THE 7 FACETS OF LIFE

MENTAL
Your thoughts, dreams, desires, knowledge, habits, and emotions.

SPIRITUAL
Morality, generosity, soul, religion, and spirituality (in whatever form that means to you).

RELATIONSHIPS
Your significant other, family, friends, and society.

ENVIRONMENT
The space around you, your residence, neighborhood, city, nature, and possessions.

WORK
Work, major projects, job, and vocation.

PHYSICAL
Your body, health, actions, activities, and hobbies.

FINANCE
Money, debt, saving, and financial knowledge.

Finding balance in your life requires an honest assessment of your current truths, a determination of what areas are out of balance, and finally taking steps to begin to correct those areas allowing more peace and harmony into your life.

In a few places you will see a number at the end of the question. These numbers refer to the references list on page 193 where you can find additional information or suggestions.

On The Cover

The open circle, or ensō, symbol from Zen Buddhism is used to represent imperfection, an unfinished journey, and personal development. What better way to think of our search for balance in life than through the ensō.

Mental

January 1

What are your top 3 goals for this year?

20___:_____

_____

_____

20___:_____

_____

_____

20___:_____

_____

_____

Spiritual

January 2

What is your biggest challenge regarding your spirituality?

20___:_____

_____

_____

20___:_____

_____

_____

20___:_____

_____

_____

January 3

Do you have many broad friendships or fewer deep friendships?

20___:

20___:

20___:

January 4

When and why did you last redecorate or rearrange your space?

20___:

20___:

20___:

Work   # January 5

What was your favorite thing to play as a child? Does your work reflect that?

20___:_____

_____

_____

20___:_____

_____

_____

20___:_____

_____

_____

Physical   # January 6

List the first action you could take towards achieving each of your yearly goals.

20___:_____

_____

_____

20___:_____

_____

_____

20___:_____

_____

_____

January 7

What was the last amazing thing that you purchased?

20___:

20___:

20___:

January 8

How do you define success for your own life?

20___:

20___:

20___:

Spiritual

January 9

How is your soul today?

20___:_____

_____

_____

20___:_____

_____

_____

20___:_____

_____

_____

Relationships

January 10

What will you do next month to help someone else achieve a goal?

20___:_____

_____

_____

20___:_____

_____

_____

20___:_____

_____

_____

January 11 _____ Environment

If you had to get rid of everything that you own, what 5 things would you keep?

20___:_____

_____

_____

20___:_____

_____

_____

20___:_____

_____

_____

January 12 _____ Work

Do you work because you're afraid of something or because you're excited about something?

20___:_____

_____

_____

20___:_____

_____

_____

20___:_____

_____

_____

Physical

January 13

The one thing that you like to do the most in your private time is:

20___:_____

_____

_____

20___:_____

_____

_____

20___:_____

_____

_____

Finance

January 14

If you could invest money in something today, what would it be?

20___:_____

_____

_____

20___:_____

_____

_____

20___:_____

_____

_____

January 15

If you had two wishes, what would they be?

20___:_____

_____

_____

20___:_____

_____

_____

20___:_____

_____

_____

January 16

Do you feel that there is a greater power in the universe? Can you describe it?

20___:_____

_____

_____

20___:_____

_____

_____

20___:_____

_____

_____

Relationships
January 17

Who are your top three friends and what do you have in common?

20___:_____

_____

_____

20___:_____

_____

_____

20___:_____

_____

_____

Environment
January 18

If you could make one positive impact on the world, what would it be?

20___:_____

_____

_____

20___:_____

_____

_____

20___:_____

_____

_____

January 19 Work

What do you like most about your work?

20___:_____

_____

_____

20___:_____

_____

_____

20___:_____

_____

_____

January 20 Physical

What has your body been saying no to?

20___:_____

_____

_____

20___:_____

_____

_____

20___:_____

_____

_____

Finance   # January 21

When was the last time you calculated your net worth?

20___:

20___:

20___:

Mental   # January 22

When was the last time you took time to reflect on your life?

20___:

20___:

20___:

January 23

What significant spiritual experience did you have last year?

20___:_____

_____

_____

20___:_____

_____

_____

20___:_____

_____

_____

January 24

What challenges do you face? Who can you ask for help?

20___:_____

_____

_____

20___:_____

_____

_____

20___:_____

_____

_____

Environment

January 25

List three things that you own but haven't seen or touched in the past year.

20___:_____

_____

_____

20___:_____

_____

_____

20___:_____

_____

_____

Work

January 26

Do you have a vocation or just a job? Why do you feel that way?

20___:_____

_____

_____

20___:_____

_____

_____

20___:_____

_____

_____

January 27   Physical

The best thing that you do for your body every day is:

20___:

20___:

20___:

January 28   Finance

Look up a financial term you don't understand and explain it in your own words.

20___:

20___:

20___:

Mental
January 29

What time of day do you feel most energized?

20___:_____

_____

_____

20___:_____

_____

_____

20___:_____

_____

_____

Spiritual
January 30

What question do you have for the living person that you most admire?

20___:_____

_____

_____

20___:_____

_____

_____

20___:_____

_____

_____

January 31

Describe the last time you sacrificed something for your significant other.

20___:

20___:

20___:

February 1

What do you wish you owned?

20___:

20___:

20___:

Work

February 2

How well does your current job fit your innate abilities and traits?

20___:

20___:

20___:

Physical

February 3

What did you do for your health last month?

20___:

20___:

20___:

February 4

What do you need to learn more about to feel more in control of your money?

20___:

20___:

20___:

February 5
Mental

Where do you see yourself in three years?

20___:

20___:

20___:

Spiritual

February 6

How well do you feel your life has been lived so far?

20___:_____

_____

_____

20___:_____

_____

_____

20___:_____

_____

_____

Relationships

February 7

Who do you most admire and why?

20___:_____

_____

_____

20___:_____

_____

_____

20___:_____

_____

_____

February 8

Do you own your home or does it own you?

20___:_____

_____

_____

20___:_____

_____

_____

20___:_____

_____

_____

February 9

What would it take to finally finish, or start, that incomplete project of yours?

20___:_____

_____

_____

20___:_____

_____

_____

20___:_____

_____

_____

Physical   # February 10

What is the biggest health threat in your family history?

20___:_____

_____

_____

20___:_____

_____

_____

20___:_____

_____

_____

Finance   # February 11

If you reduced your expenses and increased your savings, what opportunities would you have?

20___:_____

_____

_____

20___:_____

_____

_____

20___:_____

_____

_____

February 12
Mental

How many phases does love go through for you? Where are you today?

20___:_____

_____

_____

20___:_____

_____

_____

20___:_____

_____

_____

February 13
Spiritual

How much of the world do you feel is about luck, preparation or higher design?

20___:_____

_____

_____

20___:_____

_____

_____

20___:_____

_____

_____

Relationships

February 14

Express your love for somebody else without using the word "love".

20___:_____

_____

_____

20___:_____

_____

_____

20___:_____

_____

_____

Environment

February 15

What things do you pay for every month but could easily live without?

20___:_____

_____

_____

20___:_____

_____

_____

20___:_____

_____

_____

February 16

Do you excel at starting projects or finishing them?

20___:_____

_____

_____

20___:_____

_____

_____

20___:_____

_____

_____

February 17

When was the last time you exercised and what did you do?

20___:_____

_____

_____

20___:_____

_____

_____

20___:_____

_____

_____

Finance
February 18

How could you make a little extra income from your hobby?

20___:_____

_____

_____

20___:_____

_____

_____

20___:_____

_____

_____

Mental
February 19

What scared you last week?

20___:_____

_____

_____

20___:_____

_____

_____

20___:_____

_____

_____

February 20

How do you feel when you donate your time?

20___:_____

_____

_____

20___:_____

_____

_____

20___:_____

_____

_____

February 21

Are you the average of the five people that you spend the most time with?

20___:_____

_____

_____

20___:_____

_____

_____

20___:_____

_____

_____

Environment
February 22

What would you miss the most if the power went out for a week?

20___:_____

_____

_____

20___:_____

_____

_____

20___:_____

_____

_____

Work
February 23

Who at work would be the best person to balance your strengths & weaknesses?

20___:_____

_____

_____

20___:_____

_____

_____

20___:_____

_____

_____

February 24

When you exercise you feel _____.

20___:

20___:

20___:

February 25

What was the best money advice that you heard last year?

20___:

20___:

20___:

Mental
February 26

What are your top three values?

20___:_____

_____

_____

20___:_____

_____

_____

20___:_____

_____

_____

Spiritual
February 27

What was the last thing you asked a higher power for help with?

20___:_____

_____

_____

20___:_____

_____

_____

20___:_____

_____

_____

February 28

Describe the last time your significant other sacrificed for you.

20___:_____

_____

_____

20___:_____

_____

_____

20___:_____

_____

_____

March 1

What do you like best about your favorite vacation spot?

20___:_____

_____

_____

20___:_____

_____

_____

20___:_____

_____

_____

Work   March 2

Have you ever thought of starting a business? What was it?

20___:_____

_____

_____

20___:_____

_____

_____

20___:_____

_____

_____

Physical   March 3

What actions can you take to address your top two health concerns?

20___:_____

_____

_____

20___:_____

_____

_____

20___:_____

_____

_____

March 4
Finance

What was the last book/article you read, or video you watched, about money?

20___:

20___:

20___:

March 5
Mental

You know that you usually get angry when this happens:

20___:

20___:

20___:

Spiritual

March 6

What do you think the meaning of life is?

20___:_____

_____

_____

20___:_____

_____

_____

20___:_____

_____

_____

Relationships

March 7

Who influences you the most in your daily life?

20___:_____

_____

_____

20___:_____

_____

_____

20___:_____

_____

_____

March 8

Do you feel connected to nature?

20___:

20___:

20___:

March 9

List two changes at work that would make your time more efficient.

20___:

20___:

20___:

Physical

March 10

What is the calorie count of the two meals that you most often eat?

20___:_____

_____

_____

20___:_____

_____

_____

20___:_____

_____

_____

Finance

March 11

What did you do last year to help reach your financial goals?

20___:_____

_____

_____

20___:_____

_____

_____

20___:_____

_____

_____

March 12
Mental

What have your dreams been about lately?

20___:_____

_____

_____

20___:_____

_____

_____

20___:_____

_____

_____

March 13
Spiritual

What do you hope somebody sees when they look into your eyes?

20___:_____

_____

_____

20___:_____

_____

_____

20___:_____

_____

_____

Relationships
March 14

Who was the last person you asked for help? What was it for?

20___:_____

_____

_____

20___:_____

_____

_____

20___:_____

_____

_____

Environment
March 15

Do you clean things regularly or only when they clearly need it?

20___:_____

_____

_____

20___:_____

_____

_____

20___:_____

_____

_____

March 16

What career would you choose if you could pick anything?

20___:_____

_____

_____

20___:_____

_____

_____

20___:_____

_____

_____

March 17

Visualize yourself doing your favorite outdoor activity. How do you feel?

20___:_____

_____

_____

20___:_____

_____

_____

20___:_____

_____

_____

Finance　　　　　　　　　　　　　# March 18

How equal do you feel your pay is compared to the value you provide?

20___:

20___:

20___:

Mental　　　　　　　　　　　　　# March 19

List five of your habits.[1]

20___:

20___:

20___:

March 20

How often do you do the right thing when nobody is looking?

20___:_____

_____

_____

20___:_____

_____

_____

20___:_____

_____

_____

March 21

If you could help one person realize one of their goals, who & what would it be?

20___:_____

_____

_____

20___:_____

_____

_____

20___:_____

_____

_____

Environment
March 22

Describe how your residence makes you feel.

20___:_____

_____

_____

20___:_____

_____

_____

20___:_____

_____

_____

Work
March 23

How much energy do you have after a typical day at work?

20___:_____

_____

_____

20___:_____

_____

_____

20___:_____

_____

_____

March 24

Do you watch more TV, videos, or internet than you think you should? Why?

20___:

20___:

20___:

March 25

What percentage of your debt is for things that you don't really need?

20___:

20___:

20___:

Mental

March 26

You get most frustrated about _____.

20___:_____

_____

_____

20___:_____

_____

_____

20___:_____

_____

_____

Spiritual

March 27

What are your spiritual goals?

20___:_____

_____

_____

20___:_____

_____

_____

20___:_____

_____

_____

March 28

When was the last time you judged somebody that you later regretted?

20___:_____

_____

_____

20___:_____

_____

_____

20___:_____

_____

_____

March 29

When you retire, where would you like to live?

20___:_____

_____

_____

20___:_____

_____

_____

20___:_____

_____

_____

Work
March 30

How well did your last career test match what you feel inside?[2]

20___:_____

_____

_____

20___:_____

_____

_____

20___:_____

_____

_____

Physical
March 31

What did you enjoy doing when you were ten?

20___:_____

_____

_____

20___:_____

_____

_____

20___:_____

_____

_____

April 1

How comfortable are you with your level of insurance protection?

20___:

20___:

20___:

April 2

If you had to do one positive but scary thing today, what would it be?

20___:

20___:

20___:

Spiritual   April 3

When was the last time you felt joy?

20___:_____

_____

_____

20___:_____

_____

_____

20___:_____

_____

_____

Relationships   April 4

Why do you love your pets?

20___:_____

_____

_____

20___:_____

_____

_____

20___:_____

_____

_____

April 5

What could you do next month to reduce the amount of trash you generate?

20___:_____

_____

_____

20___:_____

_____

_____

20___:_____

_____

_____

April 6

When was the last time you received and gave recognition?

20___:_____

_____

_____

20___:_____

_____

_____

20___:_____

_____

_____

Physical   # April 7

Your biggest accomplishment last year was:

20___:_____

_____

_____

20___:_____

_____

_____

20___:_____

_____

_____

Finance   # April 8

How often do you create a personal budget?

20___:_____

_____

_____

20___:_____

_____

_____

20___:_____

_____

_____

April 9
Mental

The last time you woke up at night feeling anxious it was because of:

20___:_____

_____

_____

20___:_____

_____

_____

20___:_____

_____

_____

April 10
Spiritual

What one thing will you do tomorrow to be a better person?

20___:_____

_____

_____

20___:_____

_____

_____

20___:_____

_____

_____

Relationships   April 11

You have the most influence over this group of people:

20___:_____

_____

_____

20___:_____

_____

_____

20___:_____

_____

_____

Environment   April 12

Would it be better to move or stay where you are?

20___:_____

_____

_____

20___:_____

_____

_____

20___:_____

_____

_____

April 13

How content are you with your position at work?

20___:_____

_____

_____

20___:_____

_____

_____

20___:_____

_____

_____

April 14

What did you try to do last month but were unsuccessful at?

20___:_____

_____

_____

20___:_____

_____

_____

20___:_____

_____

_____

Finance

April 15

What could you learn from or teach to your parents about finances?

20___:_____

_____

_____

20___:_____

_____

_____

20___:_____

_____

_____

Mental

April 16

What are you afraid of?

20___:_____

_____

_____

20___:_____

_____

_____

20___:_____

_____

_____

April 17

How do you want people to remember you?

20___:_____

_____

_____

20___:_____

_____

_____

20___:_____

_____

April 18

What is a common misconception about you? Should you try to change it?

20___:_____

_____

_____

20___:_____

_____

_____

20___:_____

_____

_____

Environment
April 19

What is your favorite season? Why that one?

20___:

20___:

20___:

Work
April 20

What does your boss do that you would not want to have to do?

20___:

20___:

20___:

April 21

What types of activities do you daydream about the most?

20___:_____

_____

_____

20___:_____

_____

_____

20___:_____

_____

_____

April 22

How does money impact your health?

20___:_____

_____

_____

20___:_____

_____

_____

20___:_____

_____

_____

Mental   April 23

The secret desire that you would rather keep to yourself is:

20___:_____

_____

_____

20___:_____

_____

_____

20___:_____

_____

_____

Spiritual   April 24

Do you feel mature in your beliefs or are you still growing?

20___:_____

_____

_____

20___:_____

_____

_____

20___:_____

_____

_____

April 25
Relationships

Most people would say that you are _____ and _____ . Do you agree?

20___:_____

_____

_____

20___:_____

_____

_____

20___:_____

_____

_____

April 26
Environment

What was the last national park that you visited? How long ago was it?

20___:_____

_____

_____

20___:_____

_____

_____

20___:_____

_____

_____

Work April 27

What skills would you need to learn or improve to get a promotion?

20___:

20___:

20___:

Physical April 28

Think of your favorite activities. What are the common aspects between them?

20___:

20___:

20___:

April 29
Finance

The next time you are about to make an impulse purchase you will think about:

20___:

_____

_____

20___:

_____

_____

20___:

_____

_____

April 30
Mental

When was the last time your greatest fears actually came true?

20___:

_____

_____

20___:

_____

_____

20___:

_____

_____

Spiritual

May 1

What question are you seeking an answer to?

20___: _____

_____

_____

20___: _____

_____

_____

20___: _____

_____

_____

Relationships

May 2

Name a person that you would like to get to know better next month.

20___: _____

_____

_____

20___: _____

_____

_____

20___: _____

_____

_____

May 3   Environment

What country or culture do you want to know more about?

20___:_____

_____

20___:_____

_____

20___:_____

_____

May 4   Work

Do you usually wait to be directed or seek out work on your own?

20___:_____

_____

20___:_____

_____

20___:_____

_____

Physical

May 5

What did you do differently last month that felt good?

20___:_____

_____

_____

20___:_____

_____

_____

20___:_____

_____

_____

Finance

May 6

How much do you currently have in your checking and savings accounts?

20___:_____

_____

_____

20___:_____

_____

_____

20___:_____

_____

_____

May 7

When was the last time you felt in control of your life?

20___:_____

_____

_____

20___:_____

_____

_____

20___:_____

_____

_____

May 8

Living a moral life means _____.

20___:_____

_____

_____

20___:_____

_____

_____

20___:_____

_____

_____

Relationships   # May 9

Who is learning bad habits from you?

20___:_____

_____

_____

20___:_____

_____

_____

20___:_____

_____

_____

Environment   # May 10

Are urban or wilderness settings more relaxing? Why do you think that is?

20___:_____

_____

_____

20___:_____

_____

_____

20___:_____

_____

_____

May 11 Work

What would you like your next job to be?

20___:_____

_____

_____

20___:_____

_____

_____

20___:_____

_____

_____

May 12 Physical

What was the last thing that you practiced?

20___:_____

_____

_____

20___:_____

_____

_____

20___:_____

_____

_____

Finance

May 13

How has a recent purchase impacted your freedom to make future choices?

20___: _____

_____

20___: _____

_____

20___: _____

_____

Mental

May 14

What "educational" videos did you watch last week?[3]

20___: _____

_____

20___: _____

_____

20___: _____

_____

May 15
Spiritual

How does your spirituality or lack thereof impact your daily decision making?

20___:_____

_____

_____

20___:_____

_____

_____

20___:_____

_____

_____

May 16
Relationships

When was the last time you tried to change someone? Did it work?

20___:_____

_____

_____

20___:_____

_____

_____

20___:_____

_____

_____

Environment   May 17

If you had the money and it was perfectly safe, where on earth would you visit?

20___:_____

_____

_____

20___:_____

_____

_____

20___:_____

_____

_____

Work   May 18

What could you give a presentation or class on to educate your coworkers?

20___:_____

_____

_____

20___:_____

_____

_____

20___:_____

_____

_____

May 19
Physical

How many hours of sleep did you average last week and was it enough?

20___: _____

_____

_____

20___: _____

_____

_____

20___: _____

_____

_____

May 20
Finance

What is the lowest income that you could possibly live on?

20___: _____

_____

_____

20___: _____

_____

_____

20___: _____

_____

_____

Mental   May 21

Is your happiness based on somebody else's actions? If so, how?

20___:_____

_____

_____

20___:_____

_____

_____

20___:_____

_____

_____

Spiritual   May 22

What two things do you feel morally obligated to do?

20___:_____

_____

_____

20___:_____

_____

_____

20___:_____

_____

_____

May 23

What are three things that you could do for your significant other this year?

20___:_____

_____

_____

20___:_____

_____

_____

20___:_____

_____

_____

May 24

How would somebody from 1900 find your life luxurious? How about 1950?

20___:_____

_____

_____

20___:_____

_____

_____

20___:_____

_____

_____

Work

May 25

List the next three steps you would need to take to get your dream job.

20___:_____

_____

_____

20___:_____

_____

_____

20___:_____

_____

_____

Physical

May 26

How many hours did you spend doing outdoor activities last month?

20___:_____

_____

_____

20___:_____

_____

_____

20___:_____

_____

_____

May 27
Finance

What was the worst money advice that you heard last year?

20___:

20___:

20___:

May 28
Mental

What have you learned this year about your mind and thought processes?

20___:

20___:

20___:

Spiritual   May 29

What was the last generous thing you did?

20___:_____

_____

_____

20___:_____

_____

_____

20___:_____

_____

_____

Relationships   May 30

Who should you reconnect with this year? How long has it been?

20___:_____

_____

_____

20___:_____

_____

_____

20___:_____

_____

_____

May 31

Are you part of your community or are you just living there?

20___:_____

_____

_____

20___:_____

_____

_____

20___:_____

_____

_____

June 1

The most fulfilling project that you worked on last year was:

20___:_____

_____

_____

20___:_____

_____

_____

20___:_____

_____

_____

Physical
June 2

How well does your body like the climate that you live in?

20___:_____

_____

_____

20___:_____

_____

_____

20___:_____

_____

_____

Finance
June 3

Do you avoid the stock market or utilize it?

20___:_____

_____

_____

20___:_____

_____

_____

20___:_____

_____

_____

June 4
Mental

What is the first step to changing your worst habit?

20___:

_____

_____

20___:

_____

_____

20___:

_____

_____

June 5
Spiritual

Who would benefit if you recorded your life story?

20___:

_____

_____

20___:

_____

_____

20___:

_____

_____

Relationships   # June 6

Do you support your friends more than they support you?

20___:_____

_____

_____

20___:_____

_____

_____

20___:_____

_____

_____

Environment   # June 7

The one thing that you could start doing today to help the environment is:

20___:_____

_____

_____

20___:_____

_____

_____

20___:_____

_____

_____

June 8

What are the top three things that you spend your time on each weekday?

20___:

20___:

20___:

June 9

When was the last time you rode a bicycle? Do you miss it?

20___:

20___:

20___:

Finance

June 10

How much money would you need at retirement to maintain your lifestyle?

20___:_____

_____

_____

20___:_____

_____

_____

20___:_____

_____

_____

Mental

June 11

What is something that you believe in but those around you think is crazy?

20___:_____

_____

_____

20___:_____

_____

_____

20___:_____

_____

_____

June 12

Do you have a moral code? Is it written down?

20___:_____

_____

_____

20___:_____

_____

_____

20___:_____

_____

_____

June 13

Do you love your significant other because you dislike the same things?

20___:_____

_____

_____

20___:_____

_____

_____

20___:_____

_____

_____

Environment
June 14

List three outdoor activities you will do this year.

20___: _____

_____

_____

20___: _____

_____

_____

20___: _____

_____

_____

Work
June 15

How well does your job suit your personality on a scale of 1-5? 5 is best.[4]

20___: _____

_____

_____

20___: _____

_____

_____

20___: _____

_____

_____

June 16

What do you love to eat but feel terrible from after you do?

20___:_____

_____

_____

20___:_____

_____

_____

20___:_____

_____

_____

June 17

What is your best money habit?

20___:_____

_____

_____

20___:_____

_____

_____

20___:_____

_____

_____

Mental
June 18

What book is hiding inside you?

20___:_____

_____

_____

20___:_____

_____

_____

20___:_____

_____

_____

Spiritual
June 19

What religion do you want to know more about?

20___:_____

_____

_____

20___:_____

_____

_____

20___:_____

_____

_____

June 20
Relationships

The last time you surprised somebody was _____.

20___:_____

_____

_____

20___:_____

_____

_____

20___:_____

_____

_____

June 21
Environment

What one thing would you change about your community? How would you start?

20___:_____

_____

_____

20___:_____

_____

_____

20___:_____

_____

_____

Work   June 22

Do you usually give at least 80% effort at work or on projects?

20___:_____

_____

_____

20___:_____

_____

_____

20___:_____

_____

_____

Physical   June 23

The last really exciting activity that you did was _____.

20___:_____

_____

_____

20___:_____

_____

_____

20___:_____

_____

_____

June 24
Finance

When was the last time you discussed finances with somebody? How did it go?

20___:_____

_____

_____

20___:_____

_____

_____

20___:_____

_____

_____

June 25
Mental

You could control your emotions better when this happens:

20___:_____

_____

_____

20___:_____

_____

_____

20___:_____

_____

_____

Spiritual   # June 26

How do you feel when you contribute to something bigger than yourself?

20___:_____

_____

_____

20___:_____

_____

_____

20___:_____

_____

_____

Relationships   # June 27

Why is your family special?

20___:_____

_____

_____

20___:_____

_____

_____

20___:_____

_____

_____

June 28
Environment

Explain one way in which your city is improving.

20___:

_____

_____

20___:

_____

_____

20___:

_____

_____

June 29
Work

What aspects of your job can you be passionate about?

20___:

_____

_____

20___:

_____

_____

20___:

_____

_____

Physical   June 30

What changes have you noticed in your body over the past year?

20___: _____

_____

_____

20___: _____

_____

_____

20___: _____

_____

_____

Finance   July 1

Do you consider yourself to be a gambler?

20___: _____

_____

_____

20___: _____

_____

_____

20___: _____

_____

_____

July 2
Mental

Are you most often constructive or cynical?

20___:

20___:

20___:

July 3
Spiritual

List one way you can help someone disadvantaged this year.

20___:

20___:

20___:

Relationships

July 4

How do you celebrate your family heritage?

20___: _____

_____

_____

20___: _____

_____

_____

20___: _____

_____

_____

Environment

July 5

How does your mood change after you clean your space?

20___: _____

_____

_____

20___: _____

_____

_____

20___: _____

_____

_____

July 6

Are you usually busy or productive?

20___:_____

_____

_____

20___:_____

_____

_____

20___:_____

_____

_____

July 7

What new physical image of yourself would you create if you could?

20___:_____

_____

_____

20___:_____

_____

_____

20___:_____

_____

_____

Finance

July 8

What was the last thing that you bought on sale but didn't really need?

20___:_____

_____

_____

20___:_____

_____

_____

20___:_____

_____

_____

Mental

July 9

When and where did you feel most confident last month?

20___:_____

_____

_____

20___:_____

_____

_____

20___:_____

_____

_____

July 10
Spiritual

Describe your stance on spirituality.

20___:

_____

_____

_____

20___:

_____

_____

_____

20___:

_____

_____

_____

July 11
Relationships

What would be the best way to meet new people that like similar things as you?

20___:

_____

_____

_____

20___:

_____

_____

_____

20___:

_____

_____

_____

Environment
July 12

How does the natural environment around your town make you feel?

20___:_____

_____

_____

20___:_____

_____

_____

20___:_____

_____

_____

Work
July 13

List one aspect of a previous job that you really enjoyed.

20___:_____

_____

_____

20___:_____

_____

_____

20___:_____

_____

_____

July 14

List three things that you are pretty good at doing.

20___:_____

_____

_____

20___:_____

_____

_____

20___:_____

_____

_____

July 15

What did you gamble on last year? How did you feel during and after?

20___:_____

_____

_____

20___:_____

_____

_____

20___:_____

_____

_____

Mental

July 16

Write down the first sentence of the vision for your life.

20____:_____

_____

_____

20____:_____

_____

_____

20____:_____

_____

_____

Spiritual

July 17

How did you feel the last time you gave to a charity?

20____:_____

_____

_____

20____:_____

_____

_____

20____:_____

_____

_____

July 18

You really need to forgive this person:

20___:_____

_____

_____

20___:_____

_____

_____

20___:_____

_____

_____

July 19

Where is one place in your home country that you really want to visit?

20___:_____

_____

_____

20___:_____

_____

_____

20___:_____

_____

_____

Work   July 20

How is your current job or project adding to your life other than pay?

20___:_____

_____

20___:_____

_____

20___:_____

_____

_____

Physical   July 21

What activity will you definitely not do again this year?

20___:_____

_____

_____

20___:_____

_____

20___:_____

_____

_____

July 22
Finance

If you stop working, does all of your income stop as well?

20___:_____

_____

_____

20___:_____

_____

_____

20___:_____

_____

_____

July 23
Mental

What message would you send to yourself ten years ago?

20___:_____

_____

_____

20___:_____

_____

_____

20___:_____

_____

_____

Spiritual

July 24

How would you feel asking for help from a charity?

20___:_____

_____

_____

20___:_____

_____

_____

20___:_____

_____

_____

Relationships

July 25

What is one thing that you want your child to always remember?

20___:_____

_____

_____

20___:_____

_____

_____

20___:_____

_____

_____

July 26

What is your greatest possession? Why is it important to you?

20___:_____

_____

_____

20___:_____

_____

_____

20___:_____

_____

_____

July 27

Describe a recent good day at work.

20___:_____

_____

_____

20___:_____

_____

_____

20___:_____

_____

_____

Physical   # July 28

What part of your body do you like the most?

20___:_____

_____

_____

20___:_____

_____

_____

20___:_____

_____

_____

Finance   # July 29

How much credit card debt do you have? Are you concerned?

20___:_____

_____

_____

20___:_____

_____

_____

20___:_____

_____

_____

July 30

What were the results of the last personality test you took? Did you agree?[5]

20___:_____

_____

_____

20___:_____

_____

_____

20___:_____

_____

_____

July 31

How have you lifted somebody's spirit recently?

20___:_____

_____

_____

20___:_____

_____

_____

20___:_____

_____

_____

Relationships   # August 1

What was a missing piece of information that caused a recent disagreement?

20___:_____

_____

_____

20___:_____

_____

_____

20___:_____

_____

_____

Environment   # August 2

How well do your local schools function?

20___:_____

_____

_____

20___:_____

_____

_____

20___:_____

_____

_____

August 3

How do you feel about the amount of time you spend working?

20___:

20___:

20___:

August 4

If you had the tenacity to do one thing every day it would be _____.

20___:

20___:

20___:

Finance

August 5

What is the last purchase that you regret?

20___:

20___:

20___:

Mental

August 6

Why do you like the types of movies that you do?

20___:

20___:

20___:

August 7

List three things that make you a good person.

20___:_____

_____

_____

20___:_____

_____

_____

20___:_____

_____

_____

August 8

The best way for your work to help others is by:

20___:_____

_____

_____

20___:_____

_____

_____

20___:_____

_____

_____

Environment

August 9

How could your local schools utilize your time or talents?

20___:_____

_____

_____

20___:_____

_____

_____

20___:_____

_____

_____

Work

August 10

What would you have to do to take a month off? A year off?

20___:_____

_____

_____

20___:_____

_____

_____

20___:_____

_____

_____

August 11

What hobby would you like to start?

20___:_____

_____

20___:_____

_____

20___:_____

_____

August 12

Describe your spending habits.

20___:_____

_____

20___:_____

_____

20___:_____

_____

Mental

August 13

Your top three strengths are:

20___:_____

_____

_____

20___:_____

_____

_____

20___:_____

_____

_____

Spiritual

August 14

How much free time did you volunteer last year? Are you happy with that?

20___:_____

_____

_____

20___:_____

_____

_____

20___:_____

_____

_____

August 15
Relationships

Do you compete with your best friend? Is it healthy?

20___:

20___:

20___:

August 16
Environment

When was the last time you checked your smoke detectors?

20___:

20___:

20___:

Work   August 17

What big, personal project has been simmering in the back of your mind?

20___:_____

_____

_____

20___:_____

_____

_____

20___:_____

_____

_____

Physical   August 18

Does your favorite hobby relax or invigorate you?

20___:_____

_____

_____

20___:_____

_____

_____

20___:_____

_____

_____

August 19

Finance

What are you saving for?

20___:

20___:

20___:

August 20

Mental

How many times did you ask "why" yesterday? Why?

20___:

20___:

20___:

Spiritual   # August 21

Did you get more or give more last year?

20___:

20___:

20___:

Relationships   # August 22

Who was the last person that you tried to impress? Was it worth it?

20___:

20___:

20___:

August 23
Environment

How much did you follow world events last year? Why?

20___:_____

_____

_____

20___:_____

_____

_____

20___:_____

_____

_____

August 24
Work

What did you learn from your work last year?

20___:_____

_____

_____

20___:_____

_____

_____

20___:_____

_____

_____

Physical   # August 25

You know you should do less of this:

20___:_____

_____

_____

20___:_____

_____

_____

20___:_____

_____

_____

Finance   # August 26

Who depends on you for financial help? Are you ok with that?

20___:_____

_____

_____

20___:_____

_____

_____

20___:_____

_____

_____

August 27

Do you typically control your emotions or do they control you?

20___:_____

_____

_____

20___:_____

_____

_____

20___:_____

_____

_____

August 28

Who or what most inspired you over the past year?

20___:_____

_____

_____

20___:_____

_____

_____

20___:_____

_____

_____

Relationships   # August 29

Name two people you need to thank and why.

20___:_____

_____

_____

20___:_____

_____

_____

20___:_____

_____

_____

Environment   # August 30

What one physical change would you make to your neighborhood if you could?

20___:_____

_____

_____

20___:_____

_____

_____

20___:_____

_____

_____

August 31

How much effort have you put into understanding your coworker's viewpoint?

20___:_____

_____

_____

20___:_____

_____

_____

20___:_____

_____

_____

September 1

You know you should do more of this:

20___:_____

_____

_____

20___:_____

_____

_____

20___:_____

_____

_____

Finance
September 2

When was the last time you bought something just to impress somebody else?

20___:_____

_____

_____

20___:_____

_____

_____

20___:_____

_____

_____

Mental
September 3

What song best describes your life over the past year?

20___:_____

_____

_____

20___:_____

_____

_____

20___:_____

_____

_____

September 4

Where is your favorite place to relax?

20___:_____

_____

_____

20___:_____

_____

_____

20___:_____

_____

_____

September 5

What good habit has somebody learned from you?

20___:_____

_____

_____

20___:_____

_____

_____

20___:_____

_____

_____

Environment

September 6

What wall color soothes you and which stimulates you?

20___:_____

_____

_____

20___:_____

_____

_____

20___:_____

_____

_____

Work

September 7

Who would be the best work mentor for you?

20___:_____

_____

_____

20___:_____

_____

_____

20___:_____

_____

_____

September 8
Physical

Are there enough hours in the day to do the things that you must do?

20___:_____

_____

_____

20___:_____

_____

_____

20___:_____

_____

_____

September 9
Finance

What financial concepts did you learn about last year?

20___:_____

_____

_____

20___:_____

_____

_____

20___:_____

_____

_____

Mental
September 10

Was it love at first sight or love eventually?

20___:

_____

20___:

_____

20___:

_____

Spiritual
September 11

When was the last time you sat quietly by the water's edge?

20___:

_____

20___:

_____

20___:

_____

September 12
Relationships

What group would you like to join?

20___:_____

_____

_____

20___:_____

_____

_____

20___:_____

_____

_____

September 13
Environment

What does community mean to you?

20___:_____

_____

_____

20___:_____

_____

_____

20___:_____

_____

_____

Work

September 14

If you had to delegate or outsource one thing, what would it be and why?

20___: _____

_____

_____

20___: _____

_____

_____

20___: _____

_____

_____

Physical

September 15

On a scale of 1-10, with 10 highest, how well do you accept your body?

20___: _____

_____

_____

20___: _____

_____

_____

20___: _____

_____

_____

September 16
Finance

The surest (not easiest) way to increase your income would be to:

20___:_____

_____

_____

20___:_____

_____

_____

20___:_____

_____

_____

September 17
Mental

What piece of information do you wish you had today?

20___:_____

_____

_____

20___:_____

_____

_____

20___:_____

_____

_____

Spiritual

September 18

The thing that calms you the most is _____.

20___:_____

_____

_____

20___:_____

_____

_____

20___:_____

_____

_____

Relationships

September 19

How comfortable are you talking to strangers?

20___:_____

_____

_____

20___:_____

_____

_____

20___:_____

_____

_____

September 20

What was the last thing that you planted outside?

20___:

20___:

20___:

September 21

Do you have a career goal and a plan to get there?

20___:

20___:

20___:

Physical   # September 22

When was your last physical and have you been following the doctor's advice?

20___:_____

_____

_____

20___:_____

_____

_____

20___:_____

_____

_____

Finance   # September 23

How does the cost of living differ between your city and where you wish to live?

20___:_____

_____

_____

20___:_____

_____

_____

20___:_____

_____

_____

September 24

You would consider yourself an expert in _____ .

20___:_____

_____

_____

20___:_____

_____

_____

20___:_____

_____

_____

September 25

What is the best way to tell if somebody is a good person?

20___:_____

_____

_____

20___:_____

_____

_____

20___:_____

_____

_____

Relationships
September 26

Is your personality closer to your mother's or father's?

20___:_____

_____

_____

20___:_____

_____

_____

20___:_____

_____

_____

Environment
September 27

Do you have too much stuff, not enough, or just about right?

20___:_____

_____

_____

20___:_____

_____

_____

20___:_____

_____

_____

September 28

When was the last time you got overly-emotional at work?

20___:_____

_____

_____

20___:_____

_____

_____

20___:_____

_____

_____

September 29

What new, healthy meals did you learn to cook last year?

20___:_____

_____

_____

20___:_____

_____

_____

20___:_____

_____

_____

Finance

September 30

What do you feel your time is worth?

20___:_____

_____

_____

20___:_____

_____

_____

20___:_____

_____

_____

Mental

October 1

Has embarrassment held you back this year? If so, should it have?

20___:_____

_____

_____

20___:_____

_____

_____

20___:_____

_____

_____

October 2

Have you felt at peace with yourself lately?

20___:

20___:

20___:

October 3

You should really apologize for:

20___:

20___:

'0___:

Environment

October 4

What's your favorite place in town and how do you feel when you go there?

20___:_____

_____

_____

20___:_____

_____

_____

20___:_____

_____

_____

Work

October 5

List one way you can improve your communication at work.

20___:_____

_____

_____

20___:_____

_____

_____

20___:_____

_____

_____

October 6

What hobbies have you engaged in over the past year?

20___:

20___:

20___:

October 7

Are you on track to reach your retirement goals?

20___:

20___:

'0___:

Mental

October 8

List three reasons that you have to feel confident today.

20___:

20___:

20___:

Spiritual

October 9

When you silently ask for help, who or what are you talking to?

20___:

20___:

20___:

October 10

Who do you carry a grudge against and how long has it been?

20___:_____

_____

_____

20___:_____

_____

_____

20___:_____

_____

_____

October 11

How do you feel about climate change?

20___:_____

_____

_____

20___:_____

_____

_____

___:_____

_____

_____

Work   October 12

If you stay on your current career path, will you be satisfied in ten years?

20___:_____

_____

20___:_____

_____

20___:_____

_____

_____

Physical   October 13

Which of your health issues last year were caused at least in part by your actions?

20___:_____

_____

20___:_____

_____

20___:_____

_____

_____

October 14
Finance

If interest rates doubled on your debt, what impact would that have on your life?

20___:

20___:

20___:

October 15
Mental

What do you most regret from last year?

20___:

20___:

___:

Spiritual

October 16

The only thing more soothing than walking barefoot on the beach is:

20___:

20___:

20___:

Relationships

October 17

How often do you initiate communication after a disagreement?

20___:

20___:

20___:

October 18

Do you like where you live? Why?

20___:_____

_____

_____

20___:_____

_____

_____

20___:_____

_____

_____

October 19

How much time do you spend at work on non-work things?

20___:_____

_____

_____

20___:_____

_____

_____

___:_____

_____

_____

Physical   October 20

Within a three hour drive, what would you like to see but haven't yet?

20___:_____

_____

_____

20___:_____

_____

_____

20___:_____

_____

_____

Finance   October 21

Do you feel anxiety, concern, or excitement about money?

20___:_____

_____

_____

20___:_____

_____

_____

20___:_____

_____

_____

October 22
Mental

What one thing would you want to know about yourself ten years in the future?

20___:_____

_____

_____

20___:_____

_____

_____

20___:_____

_____

_____

October 23
Spiritual

How have your feelings about religion changed in the past year?

20___:_____

_____

_____

20___:_____

_____

_____

_____

_____

_____

Relationships

October 24

What was the last advice you gave to someone?

20___:_____

_____

_____

20___:_____

_____

_____

20___:_____

_____

_____

Environment

October 25

How have you made your space your own this year?

20___:_____

_____

_____

20___:_____

_____

_____

20___:_____

_____

_____

October 26

What would happen if you only spent 30 minutes, twice a day, answering email?

20___:_____

_____

_____

20___:_____

_____

_____

20___:_____

_____

_____

October 27

Have you experienced the top "attractions" in your town?

20___:_____

_____

_____

20___:_____

_____

_____

_____

_____

Finance

October 28

What business would you like to run?

20___:_____

_____

_____

20___:_____

_____

_____

20___:_____

_____

_____

Mental

October 29

What three things most impact your mood?

20___:_____

_____

_____

20___:_____

_____

_____

20___:_____

_____

_____

October 30 Spiritual

Do you think science and religion are at odds or headed in the same direction?

20___:_____

_____

_____

20___:_____

_____

_____

20___:_____

_____

_____

October 31 Relationships

Describe a fond childhood memory.

20___:_____

_____

_____

___:_____

_____

_____

_____

Environment

November 1

How well does your sleeping area invite sleep?

20___: _____

_____

_____

20___: _____

_____

_____

20___: _____

_____

_____

Work

November 2

What do you like the least about your work and could it be improved?

20___: _____

_____

_____

20___: _____

_____

_____

20___: _____

_____

_____

November 3

What festival would you love to attend this year?

20___:_____

_____

_____

20___:_____

_____

_____

20___:_____

_____

_____

November 4

How much passive income do you have?

20___:_____

_____

_____

20___:_____

_____

_____

20___:_____

_____

_____

Mental   # November 5

In what way does your favorite movie reflect your life or dreams?

20___:_____

_____

_____

20___:_____

_____

_____

20___:_____

_____

_____

Spiritual   # November 6

What does it mean to you to live in the present moment?

20___:_____

_____

_____

20___:_____

_____

_____

20___:_____

_____

_____

November 7

What political party do you most closely relate to? [6]

20___:_____

_____

_____

20___:_____

_____

_____

20___:_____

_____

_____

November 8

Where do you feel most at peace?

20___:_____

_____

_____

20___:_____

_____

_____

20___:_____

_____

_____

Work
November 9

What is the real reason that you go to work every day?

20___:_____

_____

_____

20___:_____

_____

_____

20___:_____

_____

_____

Physical
November 10

If you had to evacuate on short notice, what would you take in the car with you?

20___:_____

_____

_____

20___:_____

_____

_____

20___:_____

_____

_____

November 11   Finance

Where do you think you will be financially next year?

20___:_____

_____

_____

20___:_____

_____

_____

20___:_____

_____

_____

November 12   Mental

When was the last time you led by example? How did you feel?

20___:_____

_____

_____

20___:_____

_____

_____

20___:_____

_____

_____

Spiritual
November 13

List a benefit and a drawback you see of organized religion.

20___:_____

_____

_____

20___:_____

_____

_____

20___:_____

_____

_____

Relationships
November 14

Why do you own or not own a pet?

20___:_____

_____

_____

20___:_____

_____

_____

20___:_____

_____

_____

November 15

What is your happiest memory of being outside last year?

20___:_____

_____

_____

20___:_____

_____

_____

20___:_____

_____

_____

November 16

You could help a coworker today by:

20___:_____

_____

_____

20___:_____

_____

_____

20___:_____

_____

_____

Physical   November 17

What does your body need to function at its best?

20___:_____

_____

_____

20___:_____

_____

_____

20___:_____

_____

_____

Finance   November 18

How does your emotional state impact your spending?

20___:_____

_____

_____

20___:_____

_____

_____

20___:_____

_____

_____

November 19

What did you do last week that violated your top 3 values? Refer back to Feb 26.

20___: _____

_____

_____

20___: _____

_____

_____

20___: _____

_____

_____

November 20

What single change would make you feel like a better person?

20___: _____

_____

_____

20___: _____

_____

_____

20___: _____

_____

_____

Relationships
November 21

How many birthday greetings did you remember to send last year?

20___:_____

_____

_____

20___:_____

_____

_____

20___:_____

_____

_____

Environment
November 22

When was the last time you literally hugged a tree?

20___:_____

_____

_____

20___:_____

_____

_____

20___:_____

_____

_____

November 23

You're proud of your resume because:

20___:_____

_____

_____

20___:_____

_____

_____

20___:_____

_____

_____

November 24

What activity has been your greatest distraction?

20___:_____

_____

_____

20___:_____

_____

_____

20___:_____

_____

_____

Finance

November 25

Do you buy yourself more short term or long term rewards?

20___:_____

_____

_____

20___:_____

_____

_____

20___:_____

_____

_____

Mental

November 26

What thing outside of your control have you accepted? Not liked, but accepted?

20___:_____

_____

_____

20___:_____

_____

_____

20___:_____

_____

_____

November 27
Spiritual

What has made you feel a sense of wonder in the last year?

20___: _____

_____

_____

20___: _____

_____

_____

20___: _____

_____

_____

November 28
Relationships

What is your favorite group or organization that you belong to?

20___: _____

_____

_____

20___: _____

_____

_____

20___: _____

_____

_____

Environment

November 29

The last time you were in awe of nature was:

20___:_____

_____

_____

20___:_____

_____

_____

20___:_____

_____

_____

Work

November 30

My work skills could be used by this organization:

20___:_____

_____

_____

20___:_____

_____

_____

20___:_____

_____

_____

December 1

Could you run five miles six months from now if you wanted to?

20___:

20___:

20___:

December 2

Who is the most money-smart person that you could talk to periodically?

20___:

20___:

20___:

Mental

December 3

How happy will you be in three years if you stay on your current path?

20___:_____

_____

_____

20___:_____

_____

_____

20___:_____

_____

_____

Spiritual

December 4

How strong is your desire to help other people?

20___:_____

_____

_____

20___:_____

_____

_____

20___:_____

_____

_____

December 5 Relationships

When do you feel most loved?

20___:_____

_____

_____

20___:_____

_____

_____

20___:_____

_____

_____

December 6 Environment

Describe your happy place.

20___:_____

_____

_____

20___:_____

_____

_____

20___:_____

_____

_____

Work   December 7

Teamwork is challenging but powerful because:

20___:_____

_____

_____

20___:_____

_____

_____

20___:_____

_____

_____

Physical   December 8

Define relaxation.

20___:_____

_____

_____

20___:_____

_____

_____

20___:_____

_____

_____

December 9
Finance

List one money habit that you will start next year.

20___:

_____

_____

20___:

_____

_____

20___:

_____

_____

December 10
Mental

What did you think you wanted to be when you were ten?

20___:

_____

_____

20___:

_____

_____

20___:

_____

_____

Spiritual   December 11

Do you believe in evolution or creation? How strongly?

20___:_____

_____

_____

20___:_____

_____

_____

20___:_____

_____

_____

Relationships   December 12

Do you help or do you enable?

20___:_____

_____

_____

20___:_____

_____

_____

20___:_____

_____

_____

December 13
Environment

Do you have plans in case of a cell phone outage due to a natural disaster?

20___:_____

_____

_____

20___:_____

_____

_____

20___:_____

_____

_____

December 14
Work

Are you emotionally connected to your work? Should you be?

20___:_____

_____

_____

20___:_____

_____

_____

20___:_____

_____

_____

Physical

December 15

On a scale of 1-10, with 10 best, how healthy do you eat?

20___:

20___:

20___:

Finance

December 16

What money concept could you teach someone about next month?

20___:

20___:

20___:

December 17
Mental

What is your trick to staying calm in stressful situations?

20___:_____

_____

_____

20___:_____

_____

_____

20___:_____

_____

_____

December 18
Spiritual

When was the last time you experienced "karma" in a positive way?

20___:_____

_____

_____

20___:_____

_____

_____

20___:_____

_____

_____

Relationships

December 19

When was the last time you didn't want to visit someone but did it anyway?

20___:_____

_____

_____

20___:_____

_____

_____

20___:_____

_____

_____

Environment

December 20

What are you going to change about your residence this year?

20___:_____

_____

_____

20___:_____

_____

_____

20___:_____

_____

_____

December 21

You get most excited about this part of your job:

20___:_____

_____

_____

20___:_____

_____

_____

20___:_____

_____

_____

December 22

The single most positive change to your diet would be:

20___:_____

_____

_____

20___:_____

_____

_____

20___:_____

_____

_____

Finance

December 23

Is happiness or money more important to you?

20___:_____

_____

20___:_____

_____

20___:_____

_____

Mental

December 24

You feel the most content when you are doing _____ .

20___:_____

_____

20___:_____

_____

20___:_____

_____

December 25 Spiritual

What are you most thankful for this week?

20___:_____

_____

_____

20___:_____

_____

_____

20___:_____

_____

_____

December 26 Relationships

What are the names of your neighbors?

20___:_____

_____

_____

20___:_____

_____

_____

20___:_____

_____

_____

Environment

December 27

Where will you be on this day next year?

20___:_____

_____

_____

20___:_____

_____

_____

20___:_____

_____

_____

Work

December 28

In the past year, how has your attitude about your work changed?

20___:_____

_____

_____

20___:_____

_____

_____

20___:_____

_____

_____

December 29

What would you like to be able to do next year that you can't today?

20___:_____

_____

_____

20___:_____

_____

_____

20___:_____

_____

_____

December 30

How much money do you feel you wasted last year? List one way to change.

20___:_____

_____

_____

20___:_____

_____

_____

20___:_____

_____

_____

Mental

December 31

How do you feel you have grown over the past year?

20___:_____

_____

_____

20___:_____

_____

_____

20___:_____

_____

_____

References*

1. For more about your brain and habits, read *The Power Of Habit* by Charles Duhigg (Random House, 2014).

2. An easy and quick career test is available free, online at yourfreecareertest.com.

3. To get you started, hundreds of informative and inspirational videos are available at ted.com.

4,5. A free, online personality test is available at 16personalities.com.

6. Try isidewith.com to take a short quiz that will match you with current political candidates and parties.

*These third party references are provided as options for further infor-
mation. The author and publisher of this journal are not responsible for any
consequences that may arise from accessing or utilizing third party websites
or information.

Index

My Important Dates

_____ _____

_____ _____

_____ _____

_____ _____

_____ _____

_____ _____

_____ _____

_____ _____

_____ _____

_____ _____

_____ _____

_____ _____

_____ _____

_____ _____

_____ _____

_____ _____

My Important Dates

_____ _____

_____ _____

_____ _____

_____ _____

_____ _____

_____ _____

_____ _____

_____ _____

_____ _____

_____ _____

_____ _____

_____ _____

_____ _____

_____ _____

_____ _____

_____ _____

My Notes

My Notes

CPSIA information can be obtained
at www.ICGtesting.com
Printed in the USA
BVHW031448090119
537408BV00004B/285/P